FIENDS of the EASTERN FRONT

KILL THE CREATURES FROM HELL!

FIENDS OF THE EASTERN FRONT CREATED BY GERRY FINLEY-DAY & CARLOS EZQUERRA

FIENDS of the EASTERN FRONT

GERRY-FINLEY DAY ★ DAVID BISHOP
DAN ABNETT
Writers

CARLOS EZQUERRA ★ COLIN MACNEIL
Artists

LUKE PREECE
Cover Artist

Creative Director and CEO: Jason Kingsley
Chief Technical Officer: Chris Kingsley
2000 AD Editor in Chief: Matt Smith
Graphic Novels Editor: Keith Richardson
Graphic Design: Simon Parr & Luke Preece
Reprographics: Kathryn Symes

Original Commisioning Editor:
Steve MacManus

Published by Rebellion, Riverside House, Osney Mead,
Oxford, OX2 0ES, UK.
www.rebellion.co.uk

ISBN: 978-1-907519-24-6
Printed in Malta by Gutenberg Press
Manufactured in the EU by LPPS Ltd., Wellingborough,
NN8 3PJ, UK.
First published: October 2010
10 9 8 7 6 5 4 3 2 1

Printed on FSC Accredited Paper

A CIP catalogue record for this book is available from
the British Library.

For information on other *2000 AD* graphic novels, or
if you have any comments on this book, please email
books@2000ADonline.com

FOREWORD

DID GERRY FINLEY-DAY AND CARLOS EZQUERRA INVENT THE MASH-UP?

Think about it: their much-loved serial *Fiends of the Eastern Front* from 1980 is one of the first ever genre hybrids, blending the blazing battle action of war stories with the spine-chilling horror of vampire folklore.

Nowadays Nazi zombies and werewolf warriors are all too common, but when *Fiends* ran in *2000 AD* it was an oddity. The strip shouldn't have worked alongside *Robo-Hunter* and *Dredd's* quest to find the Judge Child – but it did.

You can credit that to Finley-Day's crazed imagination, combining disparate worlds to create a new kind of narrative, and the stunning storytelling of Ezquerra, his artwork making every outlandish moment gritty and real.

The original *Fiends* strip only lasted 44 pages, spread over ten progs. But the remarkable impact of that short-lived serial enabled it to remain in readers' memories far longer than strips that had many more episodes.

I was lucky enough to follow in Finley-Day and Ezquerra's footsteps, some quarter of a century later, when fiction publisher Black Flame commissioned me to write a trilogy of novels inspired by the *2000 AD* series.

The books were big sellers for Black Flame, especially in America where few had heard of the source material. To me, that only underlined the power of what Finley-Day and Ezquerra invented.

I also got to write a new *Fiends* serial for the *Judge Dredd Megazine*, illustrated by the talented artist Colin MacNeil. I can't claim that *Stalingrad* matches the original, but it's a respectful tribute to the original creators.

Colin and I were eager to tell further tales about Lord Constanta and his fiends, although the opportunity hasn't risen yet. But you know what they say about vampires: the undead never rest easy in their graves…

David Bishop
Scotland, 2010

FIENDS OF THE EASTERN FRONT

Script: Gerry Finley-Day
Art: Carlos Ezquerra
Letters: Jack Potter

Originally published in 2000 AD Progs 152-161

AUTUMN 1980... THE BRITISH SECTOR OF WEST BERLIN... AND A STRANGE DISCOVERY HAS BEEN MADE BY WORKMEN EXCAVATING AN OLD BUILDING—

INSPECTOR BRANDT? I'M COLONEL GRANT— YOU SENT FOR ME?

JA. I HAVE SOMETHING TO SHOW YOU. YOU WILL FOLLOW ME PLEASE.

IS THIS REALLY NECESSARY? I MEAN — BIT GRIM IN HERE, ISN'T IT?

PREPARE YOURSELF, COLONEL. THERE IS WORSE TO COME... MUCH WORSE!

THERE — YOU SEE?

OH MY GOD! IT — IT'S HORRIBLE!

FIENDS OF THE EASTERN FRONT

NEW THRILL!

A SKELETON OF A SOLDIER— IN GERMAN UNIFORM!

THIRTY-FIVE YEARS HE HAS SAT THERE, COLONEL. THIRTY-FIVE YEARS SINCE HE DREW THOSE FIGURES ON THE WALL...

THESE DRAWINGS— MOST UNUSUAL! ER— WHAT ARE THEY?

PERHAPS THIS DIARY WILL TELL US. IT IS DATED MAY, 1945— THE LAST YEAR OF THE WAR...

"MY NAME IS HANS SCHMITT, AND MY TERRIBLE STORY BEGINS IN 1941. OUR GLORIOUS GERMAN ARMY WAS PREPARING TO MOVE EAST, AND WE WERE ON OUR LAST NIGHT OF LEAVE—"

1941 THIS IS THE JOURNAL OF HANS SCHMITT

FRANKENSTEIN MIT BORIS KARLOFF

NOT A BAD AMERIKANER FILM THAT, HEH?

ACH— IT WAS NONSENSE— FAIRY-TALE MONSTERS! AT LEAST A SOLDIER'S ENEMIES ARE FLESH AND BLOOD!

Next prog: SUCK THE COSSACKS DRY!

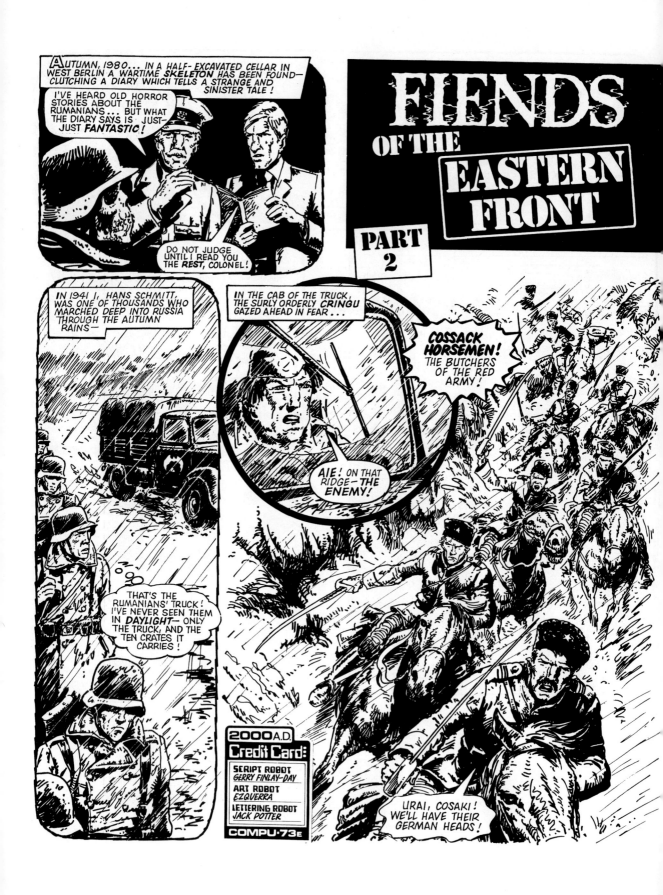

THANK HEAVEN VAMPIRES CAN'T ACT DURING DAYLIGHT!

BUT THEN THE SHADOW OF THE PLUNGING AIRCRAFT FELL ACROSS THE CELLAR—

THE DARKNESS! IT'S REVIVING HIM! HE'S AWAKE!

DEAR GOD—NO!

KA-A-WHOOMP!

THROUGH STREAMING EYES, I WATCHED A NIGHTMARE COME TO LIFE!

TH-THEY'RE ALL AWAKE! G-GOING FOR THE WRECKED PLANE — FOR THE CREW!

NEIN, IT'S HORRIBLE! THEY'RE SWARMING OVER THEM LIKE BLOODSUCKERS! UUUHHH ...

THEN, MERCIFULLY, EVERYTHING WENT BLACK!

I CAME TO HOURS LATER, IN THE OPEN WITH KARL BESIDE ME—

YOU'RE ALL RIGHT! YOU SHOULD GET A MEDAL FOR DOWNING THAT PLANE. THE MESS THE CREW WERE IN...

IT WASN'T THE CRASH THAT DID IT!

GOOD SHOOTING, MY GERMAN FRIEND! WE WILL FIGHT TOGETHER AGAIN IN THE NEW SECTOR, EH?

THEY DIDN'T TOUCH ME—BECAUSE I'M FIGHTING ON THE SAME SIDE AS THEM!

COME ON, HANS. THE RUMANIANS HAVE BEEN TRANSFERRED TO A NEW SECTOR. THEY WANT OUR REGIMENT TO GO WITH THEM. MAYBE WE'LL GET PLENTY OF ACTION TO KEEP US WARM...

SOME DAYS LATER, WE WERE A THOUSAND MILES FURTHER NORTH—

THE ARCTIC WINTER—WHEN THE SUN NEVER RISES! IT—IT'S LIKE A TRAP!

THE CHILL THAT RAN THROUGH ME WAS NOT FROM THE ARCTIC ICE—

CONSTANTA SAW ME IN THE CELLAR. HE REALISES I KNOW THEIR SECRET! I'M TIED TO THESE FIENDS NOW! THEY'LL NEVER LET ME OUT OF THEIR SIGHT... ALIVE!

NEXT PROG: THE WOLVES OF TERROR!

BUT AS THE MAN STAGGERED AWAY—

SERGEANT GORGO—BACK IN HUMAN FORM! HE—HE HAS A WOUND WHERE I STABBED THE *WOLF!*

G-GET BACK...OR I SHOOT!

LOWER THE GUN, SCHMITT—LEAD BULLETS CANNOT HARM US! YOU ARE OUR ALLY—BUT I GIVE YOU A WARNING...

NEVER INTERFERE WITH MY MEN AGAIN—*IF YOU VALUE YOUR SOUL!*

HEY, HANS! YOU THERE?

I GASPED WITH RELIEF AS MY REGIMENT ARRIVED...

YES, GERMAN—YOUR FRIEND IS HERE. HE IS SAFE...

SAFE!? YES, I AM SAFE—BUT ONLY BECAUSE WE ARE ALLIES! THERE MUST BE SOMETHING I CAN DO TO STOP THESE DEVILS—*THERE MUST BE!*

Next prog: *THE LUCK OF THE DEVIL!*

FIENDS OF THE EASTERN FRONT

THE LONG ARCTIC MONTHS PASSED SLOWLY, AS THE WAR WENT ON FAR TO THE SOUTH. I WONDERED IF THE ENEMY **KNEW** ABOUT OUR RUMANIAN ALLIES... KNEW THAT THEY WERE **VAMPIRES**!

IN 1980, THE SKELETON OF PRIVATE **HANS SCHMITT** WAS FOUND IN AN UNDERGROUND RUIN IN WEST BERLIN.

HIS DIARY TOLD THE STORY OF THE FIGHTING ON THE ARCTIC **EASTERN FRONT**, WHERE WORLD WAR II HAD TAKEN A WEIRD AND HORRIFIC TWIST...

CAPTAIN CONSTANTA AND HIS 'MEN' ...LOOKING UP AT THE SKY!

AT THAT MOMENT, HIGH ABOVE—

GO, GO, GO!

THE GERMANS WILL NOT EXPECT OUR ATTACK FROM ABOVE!

I COULD SEE NOTHING IN THE SNOWY SKY. BUT AS I TURNED...

HEY— THE RUMANIANS HAVE DISAPPEARED!

HAVE CALM, GERMAN FRIEND. LEAVE THEM TO MY MASTER— AND THANK THE FATES RUMANIA IS ON **YOUR** SIDE!

TWO THOUSAND FEET ABOVE...

SERGEANT! LOOK— A WAVE OF **BATS** COMING AT US!

THEY'RE ATTACKING US! AIEE!

NIET! NIET!

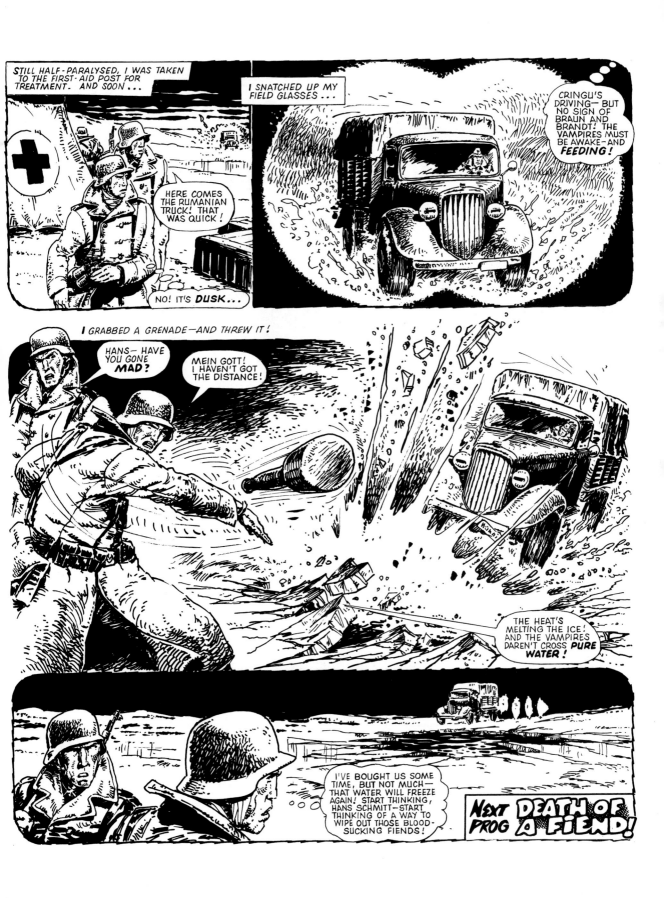

FIENDS OF THE EASTERN FRONT

PART 6

In 1980 in a ruined cellar in West Berlin, a skeleton was found — the bones of **PRIVATE HANS SCHMITT**, a German soldier. His diary told the horrific story of war on the Eastern Front — a war against soldiers who were really **VAMPIRES**!

By early 1945 our shattered army was in retreat, reeling back before the advancing Russian troops. But though the days were hellish, I dreaded the **NIGHTS** even more!

THANK GOD IT'S ALMOST DAWN — I WON'T NEED THIS **CROSS**!

MEIN GOTT! THAT **BAT**!

FLEE, YOU UNDEAD SCUM — FLEE FROM THE POWER OF THE CROSS!

SHOOTIN' AT BATS NOW, SMITHY! YOU'RE GETTING BATTLE-HAPPY!

NONE OF THE OTHERS KNEW THE TRUTH — THAT THESE RUMANIAN VAMPIRES WERE **HUNTING US**!

I SET TO WORK ON SOME BROKEN AMMO BOXES...

WHAT'S WITH THE WOODEN CROSSES, SCHMITT?

WE- WE MUST ALL WEAR ONE! THEY WILL PROTECT US...

STOW IT, YOU FOOL!

WE TRAVELLED ALL DAY, AND AT DUSK THE SERGEANT CALLED A STOP AT AN ABANDONED BARN—

WE — WE SHOULDN'T STOP HERE!

SHUT UP, SCHMITT! WE NEED TO REST...

SEEING YOU'RE SO NERVOUS, YOU AND YOUR MATE MUELLER CAN TAKE GUARD DUTY!

WOODEN CROSSES? HAH! IT'S IRON CROSSES WE WANT! HAHA!

THE OTHERS THINK YOU'VE GONE MAD, HANS! WHAT'S WRONG WITH YOU? YOU SOUND LIKE A SUPERSTITIOUS OLD WOMAN!

PLEASE BELIEVE ME, KARL— I'M NOT CRAZY! TAKE THIS CROSS— IT'S THE ONLY PROTECTION...

PROTECTION AGAINST WHAT? BATS?

BUT...

HEY, SCHMITT! GET IN HERE— ON THE DOUBLE!

TELL YOU LATER, KARL. THE SERGEANT WANTS ME...

WHAT IS IT, SERGEANT?

OH GOD! NO! THEY— THEY'VE BEEN DRAINED OF BLOOD! THE VAMPIRES ARE HERE!

**2000 A.D.
Credit Card:**
SCRIPT ROBOT
GERRY FINLAY-DAY
ART ROBOT
EZQUERRA
LETTERING ROBOT
JACK POTTER
COMPU-73E

STALINGRAD

Script: David Bishop
Art: Colin MacNeil
Letters: Colin MacNeil and Ellie De Ville

Originally published in the *Judge Dredd Megazine* issues 245-252

NOVEMBER 2, 1942.

DIE, COMMUNIST DOG!

‹ NOW YOU JOIN US IN HELL! › *

* TRANSLATED FROM RUSSIAN.

FEBRUARY 2, 1943.

< MOVE! >

< YOU'RE THE INTERPRETER? >

< YES, LIEUTENANT. **MARIYA CHARNOSOVA**, REPORTING FOR DUTY. >

< FOLLOW ME. WE HAVEN'T MUCH TIME. >

< A **PANZERGRENADIER** CALLED **RICHTER** WAS CAPTURED IN THE SEWERS BENEATH THIS FACTORY. YOU WILL INTERVIEW HIM. >

< I DON'T UNDERSTAND. THOUSANDS OF GERMANS SURRENDERED - WHY QUESTION THIS ONE? >

NEXT ISSUE: ENTER THE VAMPYR!

"OUR BOMBS TURNED THE CITY INTO A KILLING GROUND.

SEPTEMBER 27, 1942.

WATCH OUT FOR SNIPERS!

URRAAA!!!!

"THIS WAS A WAR OF TERROR WHERE ANY MOMENT COULD BE YOUR LAST.

< CHARNOSOVA. I NEED TO SPEAK WITH YOU - OUTSIDE. >*

* TRANSLATED FROM RUSSIAN.

< YES, LIEUTENANT? >

< LAST OCTOBER THE NKVD HEARD A RUTHLESS RUMANIAN OFFICER WAS TAKING CHARGE OF ENEMY EFFORTS TO SECURE THIS AREA. >

< THE GERMANS WERE SO SCARED OF HIM, THEY STARTED DESERTING TO OUR SIDE. MEN FROM RICHTER'S UNIT WERE AMONG THEM. >

< WHAT WAS THIS RUMANIAN'S NAME. >

CONSTANTA - TELL ME EVERYTHING YOU KNOW ABOUT HAUPTMANN CONSTANTA.

GOD IN HEAVEN! I HOPED NEVER TO HEAR THAT NAME AGAIN!

CONSTANTA'S LEFT US HERE TO **DIE** - HE'S INSANE.

NO, JUST FIENDISHLY CLEVER. HE'S TESTING US.

NO TALKING. **SILENCE** IS OUR BEST WEAPON NOW.

" WE CREPT BACK THE WAY WE'D COME, ALONG THE **KRUTOY GULLY**.

" IN THE RUINS WERE CIVILIANS WHO'D LOST THEIR HOMES, LIVING LIKE **ANIMALS** IN THE DIRT.

" WE WERE WITHIN SIGHT OF OUR LINES WHEN **NIGHT** SUDDENLY BECAME **DAY**.

WHO FIRED THAT FLARE? THEY'LL BRING THE WHOLE RED ARMY DOWN ON TOP OF US!

I THINK THEY ALREADY HAVE, ULRICH.

LET'S SHOW THEM THE MEANING OF BLOOD AND HONOUR!

" WE FOUGHT LIKE DEMONS, INCHING OUR WAY TO SAFETY - BUT EACH STEP COST US ANOTHER MAN.

OCTOBER 2, 1942.

HOW STRONG ARE THE DEFENCES, **RICHTER**?

FORMIDABLE, HAUPTMANN — RINGS OF TRENCHES AND **MACHINE-GUN** UNITS BEHIND BARBED WIRE.

STRANGE — THE BOLSHEVIKS ARE **DIGGING,** NEAR THE SUMMIT...

MAKING ANOTHER TRENCH?

IT ALMOST LOOKS LIKE... A **CEREMONY**.

GIVE ME THOSE BINOCULARS!

ATTACK **IMMEDIATELY**! WE MUST STOP THOSE MEN!

FEBRUARY 2, 1943.

OUR TARGET WAS THIS BUILDING — THE **RED OCTOBER FACTORY**.

THE **ENEMY** HAD BEEN SEEN RECLAIMING SPECIFIC PIECES OF **METAL** FROM INSIDE.

CONSTANTA SAID THE RUSSIAN TROOPS WERE BEING LED BY A **RABBI**.

OUR GOAL WAS TO **KILL** OR **CAPTURE** THE RABBI.

A **RABBI** LEADING A RED ARMY RAIDING PARTY? **WHY?**

IT DIDN'T SEEM **IMPORTANT** AT THE TIME. BESIDES, WE WERE **USED** TO **KILLING JEWS**...

FEBRUARY 2, 1943.

AT FIRST THE **PRISONER** WOULD ONLY TELL US HIS UNIT'S NAME: **SMERT KROFPEET**.

ROUGHLY TRANSLATED IT MEANS **'DEATH TO BLOOD-DRINKERS'**. DID HE REVEAL HIS IDENTITY?

EVENTUALLY, HIS NAME WAS **JOSEF CHARNOSOV**.

JOSEF WAS MY BROTHER! THE **NKVD** KNEW HE WAS MURDERED BY **VAMPYR**, DIDN'T IT?

THAT'S WHY **I'M** QUESTIONING THIS PRISONER!

ONCE I LEARNED WHAT THEY DID TO **JOSEF**, YOU KNEW I'D STOP AT NOTHING TO GET THE **TRUTH**!

THE GERMANS WILL BE HERE IN A FEW MINUTES TO TAKE RICHTER. YOU'VE A JOB TO DO — **DO IT**!

WHAT HAPPENED TO THE RUSSIAN SOLDIER?

'CONSTANTA **INTERROGATED** HIM FOR HOURS ABOUT **CEREMONIES** THE ENEMY HAD BEEN CONDUCTING ACROSS STALINGRAD.

'JOSEF TOLD US THE RUSSIANS WE'D SEEN ON THE **MAMAYEV KURGAN** REMOVED A **HEART** THAT HAD BEEN **BURIED** THERE CENTURIES EARLIER.

'**METAL REINFORCING RODS** WERE TAKEN FROM THE RED OCTOBER FACTORY...

'MUD WAS DUG FROM THE BANKS OF THE **VOLGA** AND TAKEN TO A **SECRET LOCATION** NEARBY...'

‹WHY?›

‹TH-THEY'RE GATHERING **COMPONENTS** FOR A WEAPON THAT C-CAN **DESTROY** YOUR EVIL...›

‹MY P-PEOPLE ARE MAKING... A **GOLEM**...›

IT WAS NEARLY **DAWN** WHEN CHARNOSOV DIED, SO WE **RETREATED** TO THE GERMAN LINES.

YOU KNOW WHAT A **GOLEM** IS?

A **MAN-MADE CREATURE** OF CLAY, BROUGHT TO LIFE BY WORDS FROM A **HOLY BOOK.**

IN LEGENDS, MY PEOPLE CREATED **GOLEMS** TO PROTECT THEM FROM **OPPRESSION.**

I ONLY SAW CONSTANTA SHOW **FEAR** TWICE: ONCE WHEN HE **HEARD** THE WORD GOLEM...

... AND THREE WEEKS LATER, ON THE NIGHT I LOST MY EYES.

THE NIGHT CONSTANTA **FOUGHT** THE GOLEM...

'FOR TWENTY DAYS WE SCOURED STALINGRAD, TRYING TO FIND WHERE THE RUSSIANS WERE CONSTRUCTING THE **GOLEM**.

'CONSTANTA INSISTED IT WAS A **WEAPON** THAT COULD CHANGE THE COURSE OF THE **WAR**.

'BUT I WITNESSED HIS **FEAR** WHEN WE FIRST HEARD ABOUT THE GOLEM.

'IMAGINE BELIEVING FOR CENTURIES YOU'RE ALL BUT **IMMORTAL**, LORD OF THE VAMPYR.

'NOW IMAGINE THE **ENEMY** IS CONSTRUCTING A WEAPON TO **KILL** YOU.

'CONSTANTA VOWED TO **DESTROY** THE GOLEM — BY **ANY MEANS NECESSARY**!'

FEBRUARY 2, 1943.

BUT YOU SAID HE'D MADE YOU **MURDER** THE REST OF YOUR COMRADES.

ONLY THE **PANZERGRENADIERS**. BUT EVEN DEATH WAS **NO ESCAPE** FROM CONSTANTA...

NOVEMBER 2, 1942.

AT LAST I HAVE THE **LOCATION** OF OUR TARGET.

AS THE MOON WANES, SO THE GOLEM GROWS STRONGER. WE MUST STOP IT — **TONIGHT!**

WITH SO **FEW** OF US LEFT? HOW?

SOME **OLD FRIENDS** WILL HELP US.

ULRICH? BUT I THOUGHT YOU WERE...

I RESURRECTED THEM. WE NEED THEIR HELP — DEAD OR ALIVE.

COME, RICHTER. YOUR MISSION ENDS TONIGHT.

'CONSTANTA SENT IN THE WALKING DEAD FIRST.

'HIS *VAMPYR* WERE NEXT.

'THEN IT WAS *OUR* TURN INSIDE THAT HELLHOLE...

KILL THE *RABBI* — NOW!

SHANTI, SHANTI, DAHAT, DAHAT!

AAIIIEEEE!

FEBRUARY 2, 1968. ATOP THE MAMAYEV KURGAN STANDS **THE MOTHERLAND**, A MEMORIAL TO ALL THOSE WHO DIED FIGHTING FOR **STALINGRAD**.

SOME BELIEVE THE STATUE WILL COME **ALIVE** TO PROTECT US IF THE CITY'S EVER **ATTACKED** AGAIN.

IT'S **TWENTY-FIVE YEARS** SINCE I CAME FACE TO FACE WITH **EVIL** AND **SURVIVED**.

TWENTY-FIVE YEARS OF NIGHTMARES AND MEMORIES THAT REFUSE TO DIE...

FEBRUARY 2, 1943.

WAS **CONSTANTA** KILLED IN THE EXPLOSION?

NOTHING **HUMAN** COULD SURVIVE THAT...

...BUT CONSTANTA **WASN'T** HUMAN.

EVEN IF HE DIED, THERE ARE MANY MORE LIKE HIM HELPING THE **WEHRMACHT**.

I KNOW THEIR SECRETS. IF THIS **PRISONER EXCHANGE** GOES AHEAD, I'M A DEAD MAN.

HOW DO I KNOW **YOU'RE** NOT CONSTANTA? OUR ONLY **DESCRIPTION** OF HIM CAME FROM **YOU**.

GOTTEN HIMMEL, WHY WOULD I LIE? I'M BEGGING FOR YOUR **PROTECTION!**

I'LL TAKE ANY TEST YOU CHOOSE TO **PROVE** I'M NOT VAMPYR, THAT I'M AS **HUMAN** AS YOU!

‹THE **GERMANS** ARE HERE FOR RICHTER.›*

*TRANSLATED FROM RUSSIAN.

‹YOU DIDN'T **BELIEVE** RICHTER, DID YOU?›

‹N—NO, OF COURSE NOT...›

‹GET HIS **UNIFORM** OFF — QUICKLY!›

‹THIS IS A LETTER FROM **STALIN**, AUTHORISING ANY AND ALL ACTIONS I CONSIDER NECESSARY FOR MY **MISSION**.›

‹YOU WILL **FORGET** EVERYTHING YOU'VE HEARD ABOUT CONSTANTA, VAMPYR AND THE GOLEM.›

‹**LIEUTENANT KAMYEN** IS NO MORE. YOU'LL DENY MEETING HIM. HE **NEVER** EXISTED.›

'FROM TODAY, I'M PANZERGRENADIER RICHTER.'

<REMEMBER YOUR ORDERS, AND BE GRATEFUL FOR THAT EMBLEM YOU WEAR.>

<FEW OF MY ENEMIES SURVIVE A MEETING WITH...>

<... CONSTANTA, LORD OF THE VAMPYR.>

THE **STAR OF DAVID** SAVED ME. IRONIC, SINCE IT COST **SO MANY** THEIR LIVES DURING THE WAR.

I DISCOVERED THE REAL LIEUTENANT'S **SKINNED CORPSE** AFTER CONSTANTA HAD GONE.

THE VAMPYR HAD WORN KAMYEN'S FACE LIKE A **MASK**, TO PROTECT HIMSELF FROM THE SUN.

IT WAS ANOTHER WEEK BEFORE I FOUND WHERE THE **GOLEM** WAS CREATED.

ITS BODY HAD BEEN DESTROYED, BUT THE **HEART** WAS STILL SAFE — READY TO BRING **ANOTHER** GOLEM TO LIFE, IF MY PEOPLE EVER NEEDED IT.

I KEPT THE HEART **SAFE** FOR MORE THAN TWENTY YEARS, BUT NOW IT HAS A NEW **HOME**.

SOME BELIEVE THE STATUE ATOP THE MAMAYEV KURGAN WILL COME **ALIVE** TO PROTECT US IF THE CITY'S EVER **ATTACKED** AGAIN.

I DON'T NEED TO **BELIEVE** — I **KNOW** IT'S TRUE.

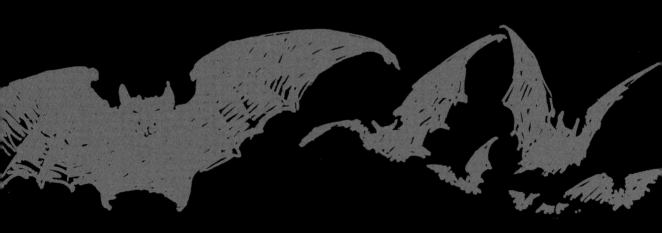

RED MENACE (BONUS STORY)

Script: Dan Abnett
Art: Carlos Ezquerra
Letters: Ellie De Ville

Originally published in the *Judge Dredd Megazine* issue 4.17

RED MENACE

'Since the distant, Pre-Atomic Era, mankind has been preoccupied with the fear that the vampire might evolve beyond its shadowy role of parasitic predator. That it might choose to use its supernormal powers to influence social or political change. That it might foment revolution. Worst of all, that it might become an instrument of war ...'
— from *A Study of Scarlet* by Martin Martinus, 808 Y.A.

MY NAME IS HANS SCHMITT, AND MY TERRIBLE STORY COMES FROM THE TIME WHEN THE WORLD BEGAN TO BURN.

OPERATION **BARBAROSSA**, 1941. OUR GLORIOUS WEHRMACHT WAS ADVANCING EAST TO BREAK THE BACK OF THE RED ARMY —

YOUNG PANZERGRENADIERS LIKE ME WERE THROWN HEADLONG INTO THE NIGHTMARE OF THE FRONT LINE.

EVERY DAY THAT WE SURVIVED SEEMED LIKE A MIRACLE, AND AN **ETERNITY**.

BY THE END OF THREE MONTHS, IT FELT LIKE WE HAD LIVED **FOREVER**, THAT WE HAD BECOME **IMMORTAL** AND BEEN MADE TO SUFFER EVERY HORROR THAT WAR COULD INVENT.

HOW **MISTAKEN** WE WERE!

THIS WAS **TOTAL WAR**, WHEN EVERY INHABITANT OF THE EARTH TAKES UP ARMS TO FIGHT FOR HIS NATIVE SOIL.

ON THE EASTERN FRONT THAT WINTER, FORCES HAD BEEN ENLISTED THE LIKE OF WHICH HAD **NEVER** DARKENED A BATTLEFIELD BEFORE...

I FIRST SAW OUR RUMANIAN ALLIES AT THE TEBLIZH RAILHEAD. IT WAS AFTER NIGHTFALL, BUT I DIDN'T MARK THE **SIGNIFICANCE** OF THAT AT THE TIME.

THEY WERE MOUNTAIN TROOPS, A FIERCE BREED, AND THEIR LEADER WAS A BLUE-BLOOD ARISTO...

WELL MET, MY GERMAN COMRADES! I AM **CAPTAIN CONSTANTA**.

SIR! WE HAVE BEEN ORDERED FORWARD TO ENGAGE IVAN'S GUNS SOUTH OF PRIPITSA.

GALLERY

2000 AD Prog 158: Cover by **Carlos Ezquerra**

Judge Dredd Megazine issue 247: Cover by **Colin MacNeil**

Judge Dredd Megazine issue 251: Cover by **Colin MacNeil**

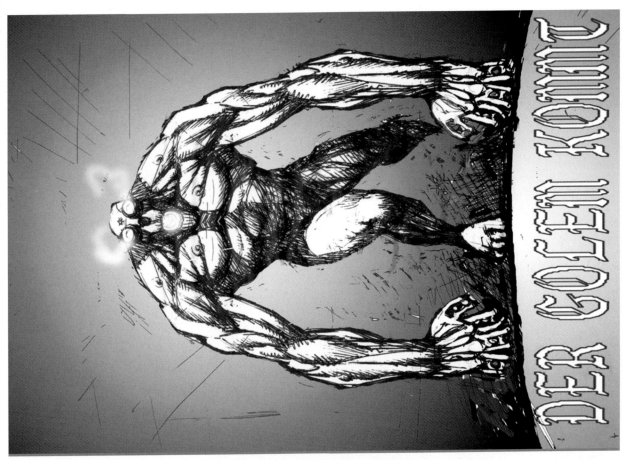

DER GOLEM KOMMT

Sketches by **Colin MacNeil**

WRITERS

One of the most prolific writers in the comic's history, **Gerry Finley-Day** holds a special place in many *2000 AD* fans' hearts as the creator of classics like *Rogue Trooper*, *Fiends of the Eastern Front* and *The V.C.s*. A keen "ideas man", Finley-Day's concepts of the horrors future warfare had in store were key to both *Rogue* and *The V.C.s'* continuing popularity, ensuring that their recent return to the Galaxy's Greatest Comic was well-received. Finley-Day also scripted episodes of *Judge Dredd* and *Dan Dare*, and co-scripted much of *Invasion!*

David Bishop spent the 1990s editing the *Judge Dredd Megazine* and, latterly, *2000 AD*. Since going freelance in the summer of 2000, he has written the *Fiends of the Eastern Front: Stalingrad* serial for the *Megazine* and an acclaimed history of *2000 AD's* first 30 years called *Thrill-Power Overload*. Now a screenwriter for the TV drama series *Doctors*, he also writes radio plays for the BBC, audio dramas for Big Finish Productions, and computer games for various developers. His short film scripts have won several awards, he's had 20 novels published and written 40 issues of the *Phantom* comic. In his copious spare time he lectures on creative writing at Edinburgh Napier University, including a postgraduate module on writing for graphic novels. You can read his blog at *www.viciousimagery.blogspot.com*

Dan Abnett is the co-creator of *2000 AD* series *Atavar*, *Badlands*, *Sancho Panzer* and *Sinister Dexter*. He has also written *Black Light*, *Downlode Tales*, *Durham Red*, *Flesh*, *Future Shocks*, *Judge Dredd*, *Pulp Sci-Fi*, *Roadkill*, *Rogue Trooper*, *The VCs*, *Vector 13* and *Venus Bluegenes*, as well as *The Scarlet Apocrypha* and *Wardog* for the *Megazine*. A prolific creator, Abnett has also written for Marvel, Dark Horse and DC Comics. He is the author of twenty novels for the Black Library, including the bestselling *Gaunt's Ghosts* series. His most recent work outside the Galaxy's Greatest Comic is DC's *Legion* and *Superman*, and Wildstorm's *Mr Majestic*. Dan Abnett was voted Best Writer Now at the 2003 National Comic Awards.

ARTISTS

As co-creator of *Judge Dredd* **Carlos Ezquerra** designed the classic original costume as well as visually conceptualising Mega-City One. He also co-created *Strontium Dog*. He has also illustrated *A.B.C. Warriors, Judge Anderson, Tharg the Mighty, Al's Baby* and *Cursed Earth Koburn* amongst many others. Outside of the Galaxy's Greatest Comic, Ezquerra first illustrated *Third World War* in *Crisis* magazine, and has since become a regular collaborator with Garth Ennis, working on *Adventures in the Rifle Brigade, Bloody Mary, Just a Pilgrim, Condors* and *The Magnificent Kevin*. He also pencilled two special *Preacher* episodes.

Since joining *2000 AD* in 1986 **Colin MacNeil** has worked on many strips, including *Chopper: Song of the Surfer* and the infamous death of Johnny Alpha in *Strontium Dog: The Final Solution*. He went on to collaborate with John Wagner on the award-winning America for the *Judge Dredd Megazine*. He has also worked on *Shimura, Maelstrom* and *Fiends of the Eastern Front: Stalingrad*, and, outside of the Galaxy's Greatest Comic, provided the atmospheric artwork on *Bloodquest* for Games Workshop. He also enjoys creating large abstract paintings. He says it's art therapy!